CW00342627

The Quiz Book

MR&MRS™

The Quiz Book

How Well Do You Really Know Your Partner?

HarperCollins*Publishers*

HarperCollins*Publishers*
77–85 Fulham Palace Road,
Hammersmith, London W6 8JB

www.harpercollins.co.uk

First published 2008

1 3 5 7 9 10 8 6 4 2

© 2waytraffic 2008

A catalogue record of this book is
available from the British Library

ISBN-13 978-0-00-729258-5

Printed and bound in Great Britain by
Clays Ltd, St Ives plc

Mixed Sources
Product group from well-managed
forests and other controlled sources
www.fsc.org   Cert no. SW-COC-1806
© 1996 Forest Stewardship Council
FSC

Contents

Introduction

How well do you really know your partner? You may feel that you have found your soul mate – that you are completely in tune with each other – but do you really know what makes them tick? Which of your habits does she find most irritating and what drives him wild in the bedroom? Who did he share his first kiss with and what item of make-up could she not live without?

These are just a few of the hundreds of fun and saucy questions that can be found in this book, guaranteed to open up your relationship to cheeky scrutiny and reveal just how much, or how little, you know about your partner's everyday habits, personality traits, hopes and dreams.

And it's easy to play as a couple or with friends – just take it in turns to ask each other a question, but remember to write down your answers so they can be compared. You can also keep track of how well you're doing by giving yourself one point each time your answer matches your partner's – then flick to the back to see how compatible you really are.

# How Well do you Really Know your Mrs?

How well do you *really* know her? Well enough to recite her favourite make-up brand? Well enough to know exactly how you should answer when she asks you 'how do I look in these jeans?' Find out in the 'How well do you really know your Mrs?' round.

1. What is her dress size?

----

2. What is her bra size?

----

3. How often does she go to the hairdresser?

☐ Once a week
☐ Once a month
☐ Once a year
☐ Far more than she needs to

4. How much does she spend on beauty products a week?

☐ Under £5
☐ £5–£10
☐ £10–£20
☐ Depends how much is in her purse

5. What is her most irritating habit?

----

6. If she had to choose a celebrity as a role model, who would it be?

☐ Jade Goody
☐ Victoria Beckham
☐ Nicole Kidman
☐ Amy Winehouse

7. If she buys a pair of trousers that need taking up, what does she do?

☐ Does it herself
☐ Pays someone else
☐ Asks her mum
☐ Wears higher heels

8. When she asks you if a new outfit suits her, what does she want to hear?

☐ She looks fab
☐ It's a bit small
☐ Like the colour
☐ The right thing – but that depends on her mood

9. Which of these would she prefer on a Friday night?

☐ Smart restaurant
☐ Cosy night in
☐ Going to the pub
☐ Sofa wrestling

10. What is her greatest fault?

----

11. What is her newspaper of choice?

----

12. Which TV programme does she think you should watch to understand her?

☐ *Sex and the City*
☐ *Loose Women*
☐ *Strictly Come Dancing*
☐ *The Incredible Hulk*

13. Who is her best female friend?

----

14. Who is her best male friend?

----

15. Which of her girlfriends has she known the longest?

---

16. How does she part her hair?

- ☐ On the left
- ☐ On the right
- ☐ In the middle
- ☐ On her head

17. What is her favourite colour?

---

18. What would she say is her best body feature?

----

19. What would she say is your 'special song' as a couple?

----

20. Most important first, how would she order these?

- ☐ Sex
- ☐ Health
- ☐ Wealth
- ☐ Power

21. What is her star sign?

---

22. What would she say is her best skill?

---

23. How would you describe her feet?

- ☐ Dainty
- ☐ Flat
- ☐ Big
- ☐ Stinky

24. Which of your mates does she like best?

---

25. You buy her a handbag for her birthday which she hates. What does she do?

☐ Asks why you didn't let her choose it
☐ Says she loves it
☐ Hides it away
☐ Beats you with it

26. Which of her relatives does she dislike the most?

----

27. What are her three favourite films?

1. _____

2. _____

3. _____

28. If she could change one thing about her body shape, what would it be?

----

29. What is the last novel she read?

----

30. Which of these best describes her skin type?

- ☐ Oily
- ☐ Normal /Dry
- ☐ The occasional blemish doesn't mar her beauty
- ☐ She's like Venus – pitted with craters

31. What colour mascara does she use?

- ☐ Black
- ☐ Brown
- ☐ Blue

32. If she were limited to one item of make-up only, which of these would it be?

- ☐ Foundation
- ☐ Mascara
- ☐ Lipstick
- ☐ Eyeliner
- ☐ You don't want to suffer finding out

33. If she were a castaway on *Desert Island Discs*, what would be her luxury item?

----

34. Which of these most accurately describes her dress style?

- ☐ Urban chic
- ☐ Smart casual
- ☐ Casual
- ☐ Scruffy

35. What is her preferred style of knickers?

- ☐ French knickers
- ☐ G-string
- ☐ Bikini
- ☐ Commando

36. What is her preferred style of bra?

- ☐ Soft cup
- ☐ T-shirt
- ☐ Push-up
- ☐ None

37. Which of these best describes her body shape?

☐ Athletic
☐ Pear-shaped
☐ Curvy
☐ Petite

38. How often does she wash her hair?

☐ Daily
☐ Every other day
☐ Twice a week
☐ When there's an 'R' in the month

39. Which of these would she enjoy you doing most?

- ☐ Stroking her hair
- ☐ Tickling her neck
- ☐ Massaging her back
- ☐ Sucking her toes
- ☐ All of the above

40. If she were only allowed to keep one CD, what would it be?

----

41. Apart from money and credit cards, what is the most important item in her handbag?

----

42. Which of these best describes her temperament?

- ☐ Moody
- ☐ Even-tempered
- ☐ Quick-tempered
- ☐ Gives PMT a bad name

43. Which of these personality groups would you place her in?

- ☐ The Healer
- ☐ The Advocate
- ☐ The Inventor
- ☐ The Terminator

44. What does she want to see at the end of a film?

☐ Tears
☐ Kisses
☐ Laughter
☐ Explosions

45. When she is upset about something, which of these is she most likely to do?

☐ Talk to a friend
☐ Confide in you
☐ Tell the whole world
☐ Throw crockery

46. Which of these would she choose for a wedding date?

- ☐ Valentine's Day
- ☐ Midsummer Day
- ☐ New Year's Eve
- ☐ Twelfth of Never

47. What would friends say is her best personality trait?

- ☐ Intelligence
- ☐ Sense of humour
- ☐ Dependability
- ☐ Knows when to shut up

48. What breed of dog would you compare her with?

----

49. Which of these best describes her self-control?

- ☐ Saint
- ☐ Small child
- ☐ Zen master
- ☐ Self-control? You must be joking!

50. How does she deal with post which she believes contains bills?

- ☐ Opens it at once
- ☐ Opens it later
- ☐ Lets it mount up
- ☐ Seals up the letter box!

51. Who is the dominant partner in your relationship?

☐ She is
☐ You are
☐ Equal partners
☐ Her mother!

52. What is her mother's maiden name?

----

53. Who is her favourite relative?

----

54. Three weeks in a row you arrive home very late after a night out with the boys. How does she react?

- ☐ Sulks
- ☐ Does the same
- ☐ Doesn't notice
- ☐ Breaks out the rolling pin

55. How would you describe her derrière?

- ☐ Pert
- ☐ Well-upholstered
- ☐ Athletic
- ☐ What's that then?

56. How would you describe her hair?

- ☐ Bouncy
- ☐ Shiny
- ☐ Frizzy
- ☐ It's in the right place

57. How would you describe her eyes?

- ☐ Soulful
- ☐ Warm
- ☐ Come-to-bed
- ☐ Scary

58. How would you describe her walk?

- ☐ Determined
- ☐ Casual
- ☐ Graceful
- ☐ Depends how much she's had to drink!

59. How would you describe her knees?

☐ Rounded
☐ Dimpled
☐ Knobbly
☐ Knocked

60. If she could only have either a bath or a shower, which would it be?

----

61. What would she most appreciate as the ultimate romantic gesture from you?

----

62. After a row, which of these would she prefer as a 'making-up' gesture?

☐ Flowers
☐ Chocolates
☐ Sex
☐ Large cheque

63. Which is the most important room in the house to her?

☐ Kitchen
☐ Bedroom
☐ Living room
☐ Whichever room I'm not in!

64. If you had to compare her to a bird, which one of these would it be?

☐ Lark
☐ Parrot
☐ Swallow
☐ Vulture

65. How does she deal with unwanted leg hair?

☐ Shaves
☐ Waxes
☐ Cream
☐ She makes you shave!

66. You have to cancel a long-standing date because of work. How does she react?

☐ Understands
☐ Throws a wobbly
☐ Sulks
☐ Life wouldn't be worth living

67. The vacuum cleaner breaks down. What does she do?

☐ Tries to fix it
☐ Asks you to fix it
☐ Calls an expert
☐ Buys a new one

68. You spill red wine all over a cream carpet. What happens?

☐ You clean it up
☐ She helps you
☐ She cleans it up
☐ She screams loudly at you

69. You have a major row just before friends come round for dinner. How does she handle it?

☐ Cancels
☐ Tells them, repeatedly, and at length
☐ Pretends everything is OK

70. You cut yourself really badly and drip blood on the carpet. What does she do first?

☐ Attends to you
☐ Cleans the carpet
☐ Hides until all the blood has gone

71. Which of these best describes her attitude if someone has crossed her?

☐ Forgiving
☐ Vengeful
☐ Resentful
☐ Be afraid; be very afraid!

72. Which of these best describes her attitude to money and financial planning?

☐ She worries
☐ In control
☐ Fatalistic
☐ She's got a piggy bank!

73. Which of these words best describes her?

- ☐ Independent
- ☐ Pushy
- ☐ Needy
- ☐ Scary

74. Which Hollywood actress does she most admire?

----

75. Which Hollywood actor does she fancy the most?

----

76. Who is her favourite rock star?

----

77. Which part of your body would she have cosmetically enhanced or altered if she could?

----

78. What is her passion in life?

----

79. What is her favourite charity?

31

80. What is her favourite item in her wardrobe?

----

81. Which type of shoes does she feel most comfortable in?

☐ Trainers
☐ Heels – the higher the better
☐ Ballet pumps
☐ Cowboy boots

82. Which one character trait would she change in herself?

----

83. What is her favourite novel?

----

84. What style of trousers does she prefer?

- ☐ Slim leg
- ☐ Bootcut
- ☐ Baggy
- ☐ Cropped

85. Which of these magazines would she prefer to read?

- ☐ *Homes & Gardens*
- ☐ *Vogue*
- ☐ *Heat*
- ☐ *Martial Arts Illustrated*

86. Which of her parents does she most identify with?

----

87. How much does it bother her if you leave the loo seat up?

- ☐ Not bothered
- ☐ A bit
- ☐ Extremely bothered
- ☐ It'd be grounds for divorce

88. Which of these is she most likely to do when stressed?

- ☐ Watch a film
- ☐ Garden
- ☐ Go for a walk
- ☐ Scream and throw crockery
- ☐ I don't know – I stay out of the way

89. Who would she most like to say sorry to?

----

90. If she were asked to nominate an eighth deadly sin, what would it be?

----

91. What is she most proud of?

----

92. What is her favourite flower?

----

93. Where is she most likely to buy a new dress for a special occasion?

☐ Designer boutique
☐ High street chain
☐ Online
☐ Oxfam

94. How long on average does she spend chatting to mates on the phone each week?

----

95. Her key to life is to:

☐ Reflect and act
☐ Have fun
☐ Go full speed ahead
☐ Sleep!

96. What is her favourite radio station?

----

97. What is her favourite perfume?

----

98. What colour is she most likely to paint her toenails?

☐ Scarlet
☐ Hot pink
☐ Pale peach
☐ Her football club's home strip!

99. How many freckles does she have?

- ☐ None
- ☐ 5–20
- ☐ 20–100
- ☐ Little Orphan Annie would be proud

100. Which of the following can she do?

- ☐ Raise one eyebrow
- ☐ Waggle her ears
- ☐ Touch her nose with her tongue
- ☐ None of the above – but she does have some tricks!

How Well do you Really Know your Mr?

How well do you *really* know him? Well enough to know what is his favourite aftershave? What he is most scared of? Which of your friends he secretly fancies? Find out as you play 'How well do you really know your Mr?'

1. What is his collar size?

----

2. What is his shoe size?

----

3. If he could have dinner with one of these, who would it be?

☐ Jessica Rabbit
☐ Victoria Beckham
☐ Nigella Lawson
☐ Dame Kelly Holmes

4. At which of these venues would he prefer to watch a sporting event?

☐ Wembley
☐ Twickenham
☐ Lord's
☐ Pole dancing club

5. If he could only have one electronic gadget, what would it be?

----

6. If your house was on fire and he could only save one possession, what would it be?

----

7. Which Hollywood actor would he want to play him in a film about his life?

----

8. What is his greatest fear?

----

9. If he were allowed to have only one film on DVD, what would it be?

----

10. Without looking, on which wrist does he wear his watch?

----

11. If he had to wear one of these, and you promised not to take photographs, which would it be?

☐ Pink polo shirt
☐ 'Rupert Bear' trousers
☐ Rubber kilt
☐ Make-up

12. If he won the National Lottery jackpot, what would be his first buy?

☐ Luxury holiday
☐ New house
☐ New car
☐ One way ticket to Rio
☐ New locks for the front door

13. Which of these would he do for charity?

- ☐ Bungee jump
- ☐ Parachute jump
- ☐ Run a marathon
- ☐ Sit in a bath of baked beans

14. What is his favourite aftershave?

----

15. How does he keep his nails short?

- ☐ Bites them
- ☐ Uses clippers
- ☐ Files them
- ☐ Gets a manicure

16. If he were to give away all his money, which of these would he choose to give it to?

☐ Animal charity
☐ Children's charity
☐ Science research
☐ Lap Dancers Anonymous

17. If he could have just one pet, what would it be?

----

18. If he stood for Parliament, which of these would he prefer to represent?

☐ Conservative
☐ Labour
☐ Green
☐ Loony

19. Which type of newspaper puzzle does he prefer?

- ☐ Cryptic crossword
- ☐ Sudoku
- ☐ Quick crossword
- ☐ Spot the Ball

20. If he had to give up one of these drinks, which could he bear to do without?

- ☐ Tea
- ☐ Coffee
- ☐ Beer
- ☐ Wine

21. If he could only keep one of his shirts, which one would it be?

22. How often does he talk about his previous girlfriends?

☐ Never
☐ Occasionally
☐ Too often!
☐ He wouldn't dare!

23. Which of these makes of car would he never dream of buying?

☐ Skoda
☐ Volvo
☐ Range Rover
☐ VW Beetle

24. If he found a £50 note on the pavement, what would he do with it?

☐ Keep it
☐ Give it to you
☐ Hand it in
☐ Head straight to the pub

25. What happens when he has his favourite sport on TV but you want to watch your favourite soap?

☐ He turns over readily
☐ He hides the remote control so you can't change it
☐ He storms off in a huff
☐ He goes to the pub to watch it there

26. How computer literate is he?

- ☐ He knows all the XXX sites
- ☐ He's fairly competent
- ☐ He can just about type a letter
- ☐ He still uses correcting fluid on the screen

27. If you were to throw a surprise party for him, how would he react?

- ☐ Happily
- ☐ Resignedly
- ☐ Angrily

28. Which of these does he dislike the most?

- ☐ Traffic wardens
- ☐ Estate agents
- ☐ Insurance salesmen
- ☐ Charity workers that stop you on the street

29. If he were Doctor Who, which assistant would he choose to travel with him?

☐ Donna Noble
☐ Martha Jones
☐ Rose Tyler
☐ K-9

30. Does he follow the instructions when assembling a flat-pack item?

☐ Never
☐ Occasionally
☐ Religiously
☐ They come with instructions?

31. How does he put his socks and shoes on?

☐ Always left first
☐ Always right first
☐ Whichever he finds first
☐ If they're on his feet, we're lucky

32. If he could represent his country in a sport, what would it be?

----

33. Which of these sporting heroes does he most admire?

☐ Ian Botham
☐ David Beckham
☐ Martin Johnson
☐ Eddie the Eagle

34. How does he view a trip to the dentist?

☐ With trepidation
☐ With enthusiasm
☐ Not bothered
☐ What's a dentist?

35. If a spider walks across the carpet, what does he do?

☐ He gently frees it
☐ He removes it reluctantly
☐ He pretends he hasn't seen it
☐ He legs it out of the room

36. Whose responsibility is it to send birthday cards to friends and family?

☐ His
☐ Yours
☐ Whoever remembers

37. Who writes your joint Christmas cards?

☐ You
☐ Him
☐ We write a bit each and sign our own names
☐ Bah humbug to Christmas!

38. How do you know if he is lying to you?

☐ His body language changes
☐ He starts to stutter
☐ He turns red
☐ His lips are moving

39. Which of these sporting events would he pay any amount of money to watch live?

- ☐ Formula 1 Grand Prix
- ☐ World Snooker final
- ☐ FA Cup final
- ☐ Grand National
- ☐ International Lap Dancing Olympics

40. How does he deal with junk mail through the post?

- ☐ Reads it
- ☐ Bins it
- ☐ Posts it back

41. Which way does he prefer toilet paper to be dispensed?

- ☐ Over the top of the roll
- ☐ From behind the roll
- ☐ Doesn't mind

42. How does he react when you ask him questionnaires?

- ☐ He doesn't mind a bit
- ☐ The whole house shudders
- ☐ Neighbours call round to complain
- ☐ The earthquake registers on the Richter scale

43. Which part of his physique does he think is his best feature?

44. If he is ticklish, which is his most sensitive spot?

---

45. Your car needs an oil change, what does he do?

☐ Changes it
☐ Asks a mate to do it
☐ Takes it to a garage
☐ Uses extra virgin olive oil!

46. How good is he at DIY home decoration?

☐ Excellent
☐ Fair
☐ A disaster
☐ Leaves it to the experts

47. How good is his memory?

☐ Photographic
☐ Pretty good
☐ Forgets my name
☐ What was the question?

48. How many of your close family's birth dates does he know?

☐ None of them, hoping they'll go away
☐ A few
☐ All of them

49. How far do his gardening skills extend?

☐ He does everything
☐ Mowing the lawn
☐ He knows how to sit in a chair

50. What is the most romantic gesture he has made to you?

----

51. Which of these would he most like to receive as a present from you?

- ☐ Season ticket for his favourite team
- ☐ Expensive wine
- ☐ Naughty weekend away
- ☐ Exemption from housework!

52. What would he do if he accidentally broke one of your favourite pieces of pottery?

- ☐ Own up
- ☐ Keep quiet
- ☐ Blame the cat
- ☐ Buy a cat and blame it

53. What particular song or piece of music brings tears to his eyes?

----

54. What programme does he think you should watch to understand him?

- ☐ *University Challenge*
- ☐ *Top Gear*
- ☐ *Match of the Day*
- ☐ *The Weakest Link*

55. The dog next door is barking all night and he can't sleep: what does he do?

- ☐ Rolls over
- ☐ Phones the neighbours
- ☐ Yells at the dog
- ☐ Buys ear plugs

56. If he loses his temper over something, how long does he take to simmer down?

☐ A few seconds
☐ Several minutes
☐ A couple of hours
☐ Until the next day

57. Which of these cocktails would he be most likely to choose?

☐ Vodka martini
☐ Singapore Sling
☐ Rusty Nail
☐ Cocktails? Give me a pint!

58. Which of these uniforms would he most like you to dress up in?

☐ Nurse
☐ Nun
☐ French maid
☐ Police officer
☐ All of the above

59. When he is out with a group of mates, how often does he offer to buy the first round?

☐ Always
☐ Usually
☐ Occasionally
☐ Never

60. Which of these household chores does he dislike the most?

☐ Dusting
☐ Washing up
☐ Vacuuming
☐ Cleaning windows

61. When supermarket shopping, does he...?

☐ Have a list
☐ Remember a list
☐ Buy what he likes
☐ Buy online

62. With which of these would he not be seen in public?

☐ Creased clothes
☐ Messy hair
☐ Dirty shoes
☐ Mother-in-law

63. The pair of you bump into one of your old boyfriends. How does he react?

☐ Starts comparing notes with him about you
☐ Sizes him up
☐ Comments later on how much better you're doing now
☐ Threatens to punch his lights out

64. When you are out walking together, how often does he hold your hand?

☐ Never
☐ Occasionally
☐ Always

65. How often does he read his horoscope?

☐ Never
☐ Daily
☐ Only if I read it out for him
☐ Horoscopes are for girls!

66. When was the last time he held the car door open for you?

----

67. Where did he take you on your first date?

----

68. What was the first football team he supported?

----

69. When he was a child, what did he dream about becoming?

- ☐ An astronaut
- ☐ A train driver
- ☐ A Premier League footballer – he still does

70. Does he keep in touch with any of his former girlfriends?

☐ Yes, all of them
☐ Some of them
☐ Just one of them
☐ Just let him try!

71. Can he programme your VCR or DVD recorder to record while you are out?

☐ Yes, easily
☐ With difficulty
☐ With the manual
☐ No way! I can't drag him away from the TV in the first place

72. If he is bored and you are engrossed in a book, what will he do?

☐ Leave you in peace
☐ Play music
☐ Try to talk to you
☐ Initiate sex

73. Which photograph of himself would he like to have blown-up and displayed in your home?

----

74. If Jehovah's Witnesses call, does he engage them in conversation on the doorstep?

☐ Always
☐ Occasionally
☐ He tells them he is having a blood transfusion
☐ He doesn't open the door

75. Would he ever shave his head for charity?

☐ Yes
☐ No
☐ Depends on the charity
☐ He'd need to grow some hair first!

76. Would he ever consider having a tattoo?

☐ Possibly
☐ Tattoo? He can't even have a flu jab!
☐ Definitely
☐ Already got one

77. Would he ever consider having his body pierced?

☐ Definitely
☐ Depends where
☐ No way!

78. How would you describe his hands?

☐ Elegant
☐ Workmanlike
☐ Artistic
☐ Stubby

79. How would you describe his nose?

☐ Aquiline
☐ Snub
☐ Big
☐ Runny

80. How does he react to change?

☐ Embraces it
☐ Resists it
☐ Goes with it
☐ He's usually the one who initiates it

81. Which of these terms best describes him?

- ☐ Team player
- ☐ Loner
- ☐ Leader

82. How does he react to strangers?

- ☐ Quite shy
- ☐ Not interested
- ☐ Very friendly, particularly if they're female
- ☐ Asks them home

83. How does he react when faced with a decision?

- ☐ Chooses on impulse
- ☐ Slow consideration
- ☐ Becomes indecisive
- ☐ Sensibly asks me what I think

84. Which of these interest him most?

- ☐ Causes
- ☐ Effects
- ☐ Correlations
- ☐ Beer

85. How does he assess other people?

- ☐ Gut reaction
- ☐ Slow consideration
- ☐ On first impressions

86. When he wants to show his affection physically, what is he most likely to do?

- ☐ Hold your hand
- ☐ Give you a pat on the back
- ☐ Hug you
- ☐ Initiate sex

87. How long does he spend in front of the mirror?

☐ Longer than me
☐ Long enough to check his looks
☐ Can't walk past one without striking a pose
☐ Mirrors are for girls

88. Is he a conformist or a rebel?

☐ Conformist
☐ Rebel
☐ Depends what I tell him to be!

89. If he were to emigrate, which country would he like to go to?

----

90. If money were no object, what would be his dream car?

---

91. Which of his habits do you find most irritating?

---

92. What sort of underwear does he favour wearing?

- ☐ Briefs
- ☐ Boxers
- ☐ Going commando
- ☐ Yours!

93. If he were to have one part of his body altered by plastic surgery, what would it be?

---

94. Besides shampoo and conditioner, what other hair products does he use?

---

95. Which of these is he most scared of?

- ☐ Dentists
- ☐ Spiders
- ☐ Injections
- ☐ Your mother!

96. Where would be his ideal place for a romantic walk with you?

- ☐ On the beach
- ☐ In the hills
- ☐ In a rainy park
- ☐ To the pub

97. Which of these TV personalities does he find most annoying?

- ☐ Graham Norton
- ☐ Anne Robinson
- ☐ Jonathan Ross
- ☐ John Barrowman

98. How long does it take him to get ready to go out for a party?

☐ Under 30 minutes
☐ 30 mins–1 hour
☐ Over 1 hour

99. Would he ever wear a vest or T-shirt under his shirt?

☐ Never
☐ Depends how cold it is
☐ Always – even in summer!

100. Which of these would be his nightmare holiday?

- ☐ Beach
- ☐ Ski
- ☐ Cruise
- ☐ Anywhere with children

Mr & Mrs
in the Kitchen

Which one of you fancies yourselves as the next
Gordon Ramsay or Jamie Oliver? Does he use
every pan in the kitchen to make a simple meal?
Or have you ever lied about liking her cooking?
Hide all sharp implements as we take Mr & Mrs
into the kitchen.

1. What is your partner's favourite meat for a traditional Sunday lunch?

- ☐ Beef
- ☐ Pork
- ☐ Lamb
- ☐ Chicken

2. What is your partner's signature dish?

----

3. How tidy is your partner while cooking?

- ☐ Extremely
- ☐ Reasonably
- ☐ Uses every utensil

4. How hot does your partner like a curry?

- ☐ Phal – scorchio!
- ☐ Vindaloo
- ☐ Madras
- ☐ Korma – followed by a glass of water

5. How would you describe your partner's cooking?

- ☐ Competent
- ☐ Safe
- ☐ Creative
- ☐ Inedible

6. How often does your partner clean out the fridge?

- ☐ Regularly
- ☐ Sometimes
- ☐ Doesn't it clean itself?

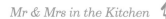

7. How well in advance does your partner prepare when cooking a meal for guests?

☐ Hours ahead
☐ An hour or so
☐ Very last minute
☐ That's my job!

8. How often does your partner empty the dishwasher?

---

9. Which celebrity chef does your partner most admire?

---

10. Which celebrity chef does your partner find most irritating?

----

11. Which is your partner's favourite kitchen gadget?

----

12. Which of these would your partner most prefer for a weekday breakfast?

☐ Porridge
☐ Cornflakes
☐ Fresh fruit
☐ Lots of black coffee

Mr & Mrs in the Kitchen

13. How often does your partner put empty cartons back in the fridge?

☐ Never
☐ Regularly
☐ Sometimes

14. Who would your partner most like to share a kitchen with?

----

15. How would you describe your partner's demeanour at the breakfast table?

☐ Silent
☐ Moody
☐ Affable
☐ Very chatty

16. Which of these juices would your partner most prefer at breakfast?

☐ Orange
☐ Grapefruit
☐ Apple
☐ Cranberry

17. Which of these kitchen chores does your partner dislike the most?

☐ Taking out the rubbish
☐ Putting away shopping
☐ Cleaning the hob
☐ Cleaning the floor

18. How often do you share a meal together?

- ☐ Every day
- ☐ Twice a week
- ☐ Every week
- ☐ Only when we have to

19. What is your partner's most irritating habit in the kitchen?

---

20. How quickly does your partner clear the plates from the table after a meal?

- ☐ Immediately
- ☐ In 5 minutes
- ☐ After a few hours
- ☐ As soon as they've been asked – at least twice

21. Which of these is your partner's essential accompaniment to egg and chips?

☐ Brown sauce
☐ Tomato sauce
☐ Mayonnaise
☐ Vinegar

22. How good is your partner at slicing a crusty loaf?

☐ Expert
☐ Not bad
☐ Doesn't it come already sliced?

23. What would your partner prefer for Christmas lunch?

- ☐ Roast turkey
- ☐ Beef Wellington
- ☐ Nut roast
- ☐ A nice meaty thigh

24. How does your partner like a steak to be cooked?

- ☐ Well done
- ☐ Medium
- ☐ Medium rare
- ☐ Rare

25. Would your partner be absolutely unable to eat any of the following?

☐ Brussels sprouts
☐ Kidneys
☐ Tripe
☐ Jellied eels

26. What does your partner prefer while preparing a meal?

☐ Glass of water
☐ Glass of wine
☐ Glass of sherry
☐ All of the above!

27. Your partner has cooked enough for two and you bring home some friends: what do they do?

- ☐ Add more veggies
- ☐ Decide you'll all eat out
- ☐ Ring for a pizza
- ☐ Throw a wobbly

28. What is your partner's favourite flavour of ice cream?

- ☐ Vanilla
- ☐ Chocolate
- ☐ Strawberry
- ☐ Any so long as it's Ben & Jerry's

29. What type of chocolate does your partner prefer?

☐ White
☐ Milk
☐ Plain
☐ Not fussy as long as there's lots

30. Which of these pizza toppings does your partner dislike?

☐ Anchovy
☐ Pineapple
☐ Artichoke
☐ Ground beef

31. How often does your partner replace the rubbish bag having taken out the old one?

- ☐ Without fail
- ☐ Usually
- ☐ Sometimes
- ☐ Never

32. If you are having eggs for breakfast, how is your partner most likely to serve them?

- ☐ Scrambled
- ☐ Boiled
- ☐ Omelette
- ☐ Poached

33. What sort of coffee would your partner prefer?

- ☐ Latte
- ☐ Black filter
- ☐ Espresso
- ☐ Cappuccino

34. Which is your partner's favourite cook book?

---

35. Which of these is your partner least likely to clean?

- ☐ Toaster
- ☐ Microwave
- ☐ Oven shelves
- ☐ Inside of the bin

36. Would your partner have any moral qualms about eating GM food?

☐ Definitely
☐ A few
☐ None at all
☐ Thought GM made cars!

37. You have hosted a dinner party and your guests overstay their welcome. Does your partner...?

☐ Quietly disappear
☐ Tactfully ask them to go
☐ Stick it out
☐ Start singing 'Show me the way to go home'

38. Which of these describes your partner's eating habits?

☐ Finicky
☐ Bit fussy
☐ Locusts and gannets could watch and learn!

39. Which of these kitchen gadgets would your partner want the most?

☐ Ice cream maker
☐ Bread maker
☐ Espresso machine
☐ Deep fat fryer

Mr & Mrs in the Kitchen

40. How often does your partner offer to do the washing up?

- ☐ Never
- ☐ After every meal
- ☐ Depends who cooked
- ☐ Only when they have broken the dishwasher

41. What is your partner's favourite fruit?

----

42. What is your partner's favourite vegetable?

----

43. If your partner had to eat one of these meals for lunch every day, which would they prefer?

☐ Chicken salad
☐ Pie and mash
☐ Sushi
☐ Burger and chips

44. What condiment does your partner prefer on a bacon sandwich?

☐ Tomato ketchup
☐ Brown sauce
☐ Mustard
☐ What's a condiment?

45. What is your partner's favourite herb?

----

46. Which of these would your partner most prefer for a weekend breakfast?

☐ Full English
☐ Kedgeree
☐ Waffles and syrup
☐ Fresh fruit

47. When you are both preparing a meal together, who takes charge?

----

48. Which of you is most likely to suggest defrosting the fridge?

----

49. If your partner could only keep one cooking utensil, what would it be?

----

50. There is one slice of pizza left in the box and you both reach for it at the same time. Who gets it?

☐ I do
☐ My partner does
☐ Share it
☐ Fight over it

51. What particular piece of music or album does your partner like to cook to?

----

52. If money were no object, what one change would your partner make to your kitchen?

----

53. Which of these best describes your partner's attitude to recipes?

☐ Follow them to the letter
☐ Use them as a basis
☐ Ignore them
☐ Indignantly ask if I think their name is Delia

54. What food treat can your partner not do without?

----

55. How many times a week does your partner prepare your main meal?

----

56. How often does your partner clean the kitchen floor?

☐ Never
☐ Daily
☐ Once a week
☐ When they are asked

57. Which celebrity would your partner most like to cook dinner for?

----

58. Faced with a choice between washing or drying up, which would your partner choose?

----

59. Which of you is most likely to cook the spicier chilli con carne?

----

60. Which of these cheeses would your partner say is not French?

☐ Roquefort
☐ Camembert
☐ Provolone
☐ Saint Agur

61. Your partner wants to cook you a meal to say 'sorry'; what would it be?

---

62. How important is warming the plates to your partner?

☐ Essential
☐ Quite important
☐ Never bothers
☐ Plates? We always eat out of the cartons!

63. How does your partner like potatoes to be served?

☐ Chips
☐ Buttered new
☐ Roast
☐ Salt 'n' Vinegar crisps

64. How happy is your partner to cook in full view of your guests?

☐ Loves it
☐ OK about it
☐ Would prefer not to
☐ Only when naked

65. What is your partner's favourite cheese?

----

66. If you were planning a new kitchen, which of these features would your partner want the most?

☐ Boiling water on tap
☐ Ice cube dispenser
☐ Self-close drawers
☐ Integrated TV

67. Which of your partner's table manners, or lack of them, do you find most irritating?

----

68. How would you rate your partner's commitment to recycling in the kitchen?

- ☐ Top marks
- ☐ Spasmodic
- ☐ Not interested
- ☐ They prepare the same meal every time they cook

69. What type of takeaway would be your partner's first choice?

- ☐ Pizza
- ☐ Chinese
- ☐ Indian
- ☐ Fish and chips

70. If you asked your partner to pass you the mezzaluna, where would they look?

- ☐ In the fridge
- ☐ In the utensil drawer
- ☐ In the garden
- ☐ In the night sky

71. Which drink does your partner prefer with their breakfast?

- ☐ Tea
- ☐ Coffee
- ☐ Hot chocolate
- ☐ Vodka and tonic

72. What does your partner think about the statement that a woman should 'be a cook in the kitchen and a whore in the bedroom'?

☐ Agrees
☐ A woman should be a princess everywhere
☐ Where's the kitchen?
☐ If I dared say that, they'd leave!

73. Which of these bad kitchen habits drives your partner nuts?

☐ Leaving dirty dishes in the sink
☐ Not wringing out the dishcloth
☐ Never emptying the dishwasher
☐ Leaving the plug blocked

74. Which of these does your partner prefer to cook on?

- ☐ Gas
- ☐ Electricity
- ☐ BBQ
- ☐ Prefers me to cook

75. Which of these dishes would your partner say originates in Greece?

- ☐ Lasagne
- ☐ Paella
- ☐ Kleftiko
- ☐ Stroganoff

Mr & Mrs in the Bedroom

Mr & Mrs is about to go behind closed doors and reveal a few home truths! From the mild 'which side of the bed does your partner sleep on?' to the wild 'which animal would you compare them to in bed?', prepare to blush as Mr & Mrs enters the bedroom...

1. How many lovers has your partner admitted to having?

----

2. How does your partner prefer to sleep?

☐ On their back
☐ On the right side
☐ On the left side
☐ On their own

3. You are in bed asleep, and an intruder breaks in. What does your partner do first?

☐ Investigates
☐ Makes you go
☐ Pulls the covers up and tries to ignore it
☐ Calls the police

4. Which word best describes your partner in bed?

☐ Considerate
☐ Passionate
☐ Willing
☐ Comatose

5. What does your partner think is the sexiest film bedroom scene ever?

----

6. Which sexual position does your partner enjoy the most?

☐ Missionary
☐ Woman on top
☐ Side by side
☐ Any in front of the TV

7. What does your partner prefer to wear in bed?

☐ Pyjamas
☐ Nothing
☐ Nightshirt
☐ Handcuffs

8. Your partner's alarm goes off for an early call. Do they...?

☐ Switch to snooze
☐ Get up immediately
☐ Get up very slowly
☐ Ask you to turn it off and go back to sleep

9. How much of the available cupboard and drawer space in your bedroom is commandeered by your partner?

☐ Less that 25%
☐ 25–50%
☐ 50–75%
☐ More than 75%

10. In a perfect world, how often would your partner like to have sex?

☐ Every waking minute
☐ 3 times a week
☐ Once a month
☐ Once *Big Brother* is over

11. Which of these would your partner prefer to have in bed?

- ☐ Wild sex
- ☐ Massage
- ☐ Breakfast
- ☐ Forty winks

12. When your partner undresses for bed, do they leave their clothes...?

- ☐ All over the floor
- ☐ Neatly in the wardrobe
- ☐ Flung over a chair
- ☐ For you to tidy

13. How many pairs of shoes does your partner have in the wardrobe?

----

14. Which of these is your partner most likely to enjoy reading in bed before turning out the light?

☐ A daily newspaper
☐ A good book
☐ A saucy magazine
☐ A bank statement

15. How does your partner like to leave the bedroom window at night?

☐ Shut tight
☐ Just ajar
☐ Wide open

16. What temperature does your partner like the bedroom to be?

☐ Like a furnace
☐ Comfortably warm
☐ Slightly chilly
☐ Not too cold – it makes things shrivel

17. When sleeping alone, which of these is your partner most likely to take to bed?

☐ A stiff drink
☐ A cuddly toy
☐ A good book
☐ A neighbour

18. What is the funniest thing your partner has ever said while sleep talking?

----

19. What was the last thing your partner stole from a hotel bedroom?

----

20. Given a free rein, what colour would your partner paint the bedroom?

----

21. Left to their own devices, how often would your partner change the bed linen?

☐ Twice a week
☐ Once a week
☐ Once a month
☐ When it sprouts legs and walks to the washing machine

22. How do you feel about the state of your partner's pillow?

- ☐ Very fresh
- ☐ OK
- ☐ Manky
- ☐ I try not to think about it

23. When does your partner like to make the bed after getting up in the morning?

- ☐ Immediately
- ☐ Later in the day
- ☐ Bedtime
- ☐ Do what to the bed?

24. At what period of the day is your partner usually at their most amorous?

☐ Early morning
☐ When they get home
☐ Evening
☐ Morning, noon and night

25. What is the most memorable place the pair of you have made love?

----

26. If it was between a favourite TV show or an early night, what would your partner choose?

----

27. What colour underwear sets your partner's pulse racing?

- ☐ White
- ☐ Red
- ☐ Black
- ☐ Purple

28. Which of these is your partner's most erogenous zone?

- ☐ Nape of the neck
- ☐ Under the ears
- ☐ Behind the knee
- ☐ Inside the elbow

29. What does your partner like to use to set the mood in the bedroom?

☐ Music
☐ Subtle lighting
☐ Candles
☐ Whipped cream

30. How many pillows does your partner like to sleep on?

☐ One
☐ Two
☐ Three
☐ More than three

31. Does your partner fantasise about someone else when you are making love?

☐ Often
☐ Sometimes
☐ They wouldn't dare!
☐ I don't know – I'm too busy fantasising myself

32. Have either of you joined the 'Mile High Club'?

☐ I have
☐ Partner has
☐ We did together

33. How would your partner react if you asked them to handcuff you to the bed?

- ☐ Surprised
- ☐ Nervously
- ☐ Cautiously
- ☐ It's a fair cop – slap them on!

34. What is the worst injury your partner has sustained while romping in the bedroom?

----

35. What part of your partner's nightly going-to-bed routine irritates you the most?

----

36. How would your partner react if the couple in the next hotel room indulged in noisy nocturnal activities?

☐ Ignore them
☐ Listen to them
☐ Compete with them
☐ Give them marks out of 10 at breakfast the next day

37. How would your partner react if you started sucking their toes?

☐ Get the giggles
☐ Kick you away
☐ Ask for more
☐ Ask if they're in the right room

38. Would either of you allow a pet to sleep on the bed with you?

☐ Both would
☐ I would
☐ They would
☐ Neither would

39. Which does your partner prefer in a hotel bedroom?

☐ Double bed
☐ Twin beds
☐ Does not mind
☐ Hammocks

40. You are both having a Sunday morning lie-in and the doorbell rings, who answers it?

☐ You do
☐ Partner does
☐ You take it in turns
☐ You both ignore it

41. Which item of their clothing would your partner like to dress you up in?

42. A wrong number telephone call wakes you at 2 a.m., how does your partner react to the caller?

☐ Politely
☐ With restraint
☐ Swears at them

43. On average, which of you is the first to get out of bed at the weekend?

----

44. What would be your first thought if your partner came into the bedroom with a spray can of cream?

- ☐ Fruit salad
- ☐ No strawberries?
- ☐ The mess
- ☐ Bring it on!
- ☐ They've forgotten their glasses

45. Which of your bedtime habits does your partner find most irritating?

☐ Hogging the duvet
☐ Ice cold feet
☐ Freezing hands
☐ Prodding them awake to chat

46. What keeps your partner awake at night worrying?

----

47. How much noise does your partner make in bed?

☐ Quiet as a mouse
☐ Noisy as a boiling kettle
☐ Loud as a building site
☐ Like a jumbo jet taking off

48. Which animal best describes your partner in bed?

- ☐ Tiger
- ☐ Rabbit
- ☐ Sloth
- ☐ Dodo

49. What is the longest time your partner has gone without sex?

- ☐ A day
- ☐ A week
- ☐ A month
- ☐ Longer than a month

50. What would be your partner's reaction if you had to sleep in bunk beds?

☐ Insist on the bottom one
☐ Grab the top one
☐ Suggest you both sleep in one
☐ Refuse to sleep in either

51. Which of these does your partner find most exciting when worn against the skin?

☐ Silk
☐ Leather
☐ Latex
☐ You

52. Who does your partner have a photograph of beside the bed?

☐ You
☐ A family member
☐ A pet
☐ Doesn't have one

53. What is your partner's worst habit in bed?

☐ Snoring
☐ Breaking wind
☐ Dribbling
☐ Having a headache
☐ All of the above

54. How many hours sleep a night does your partner need to avoid becoming tetchy?

☐ Six
☐ Eight
☐ Twelve
☐ There aren't enough hours in a day

55. On average, how many times a year does your partner stomp off to sleep in another room because of a row?

☐ Once a week
☐ Every few months
☐ Once a year
☐ Never

56. If you said you had seen a ghost at the bottom of the bed, what would be your partner's reaction?

☐ Hide under the covers
☐ Ask if I'd been drinking
☐ Start singing the *Ghostbusters* theme
☐ Sleep in the spare room

57. Which of these fruits would your partner most like to share with you in bed?

☐ Mango
☐ Banana
☐ Strawberries
☐ Dates

58. How many times a night on average does your partner have to answer a 'call of nature'?

- ☐ Three or more
- ☐ Twice
- ☐ Once
- ☐ Never, they're like a camel

59. You have gone to bed early and your partner comes in late after a night out; do they...?

- ☐ Tiptoe about
- ☐ Crash noisily into bed
- ☐ Wake you by asking if you are awake
- ☐ Sleep in another room

60. If money were no object, which of these would your partner most like to add to your bedroom?

☐ En suite shower
☐ Water bed
☐ Mirrored ceiling
☐ Single beds

61. How often do you and your partner go to bed at the same time?

☐ Always
☐ Usually
☐ Rarely
☐ Only when it can't be avoided

62. What type of bed linen does your partner prefer?

- ☐ Dark and sexy
- ☐ Crisp and white
- ☐ Soft pastels
- ☐ Rubber

63. How often do you wake up in a close snuggle in the morning?

- ☐ Always
- ☐ Usually
- ☐ Never
- ☐ Only in winter

64. Which radio station does your partner like to listen to first thing in the morning?

☐ Radio 1
☐ Radio 4
☐ Local radio
☐ Other

65. Does your partner have a preferred side of the bed to sleep on?

☐ Always on the right
☐ Always on the left
☐ We alternate
☐ Completely random
☐ They hog the lot!

66. You are both reading in bed; how does your partner react when you turn off your light to go to sleep?

☐ Turns off their light
☐ Goes on reading for hours
☐ Reads for another minute
☐ Takes it as a cue for sex

67. How light a sleeper is your partner?

☐ Wakes at the slightest sound
☐ Can sleep through most things
☐ Takes a bomb to wake them

68. What would your partner think of the statement that sex can't be fantastic unless it's true love?

☐ Agrees
☐ What's fantastic sex?
☐ Can't be true love unless the sex is fantastic!

69. What would your partner do if they discovered you phoning a sex line?

☐ Switch to conference call
☐ Cut the phone line
☐ Cut off something vital
☐ Leave home

70. How often have you been turned on by watching a saucy film together?

- ☐ Regularly
- ☐ Never together, but on my own
- ☐ We prefer to make our own
- ☐ We love *The Sound of Music*!

71. Which does your partner prefer when making love?

- ☐ Candle light
- ☐ All the lights on
- ☐ Lights off
- ☐ Doesn't mind 'cos they've got a blindfold on!

72. How do you feel about swapping pillows with your partner?

☐ We don't have 'his 'n' her' pillows
☐ Not bothered
☐ Prefer my own pillow
☐ Absolutely not! My pillow is a temple

73. What porn star names would you choose for each other?

----

74. Where and when was the first occasion that you spent the whole night together?

75. If your partner were to perform a strip for you, what two articles of clothing would you get a kick out of them leaving on?

Mr & Mrs
Out and About

When you go out for a meal where does he like to take you? To a fancy restaurant or the local burger joint? What is his ideal holiday – chilling by the pool, fine wine and culture or a boozy week away with his mates? Put on your Sunday best as we take Mr & Mrs out and about.

1. When flying off on holiday, how early does your partner like to get to the airport?

☐ 2–3 hours before the desk opens
☐ 1 hour before the desk closes
☐ Half an hour before the flight's due to take off
☐ Likes to camp in the airport the night before

2. Which type of restaurant would your partner prefer?

☐ Thai
☐ Lebanese
☐ French
☐ Italian

3. What is the most awe-inspiring geographical feature your partner has visited?

----

4. The person behind you in the cinema is constantly talking: who would ask them to be quiet?

☐ You
☐ Your partner
☐ Neither
☐ You would fetch the management

5. Which mode of transport does your partner dislike using the most?

☐ Bus
☐ Train
☐ Aeroplane
☐ Tandem

6. You are both invited to a party but your partner dislikes the host: what would they do?

- ☐ Grin and bear it
- ☐ Fake an illness
- ☐ Arrange a clashing appointment
- ☐ Suggest you go alone

7. What is your partner's patience like when visiting an art gallery?

- ☐ Endless
- ☐ Moderate
- ☐ Non-existent

8. Has your partner ever visited a fortune teller?

- ☐ Never
- ☐ Once when drunk
- ☐ Goes all the time

9. Which of these live performances would your partner prefer to see?

☐ Opera
☐ Ballet
☐ Chippendales
☐ Mud wrestling

10. Which of these would your partner fancy for a dirty weekend?

☐ Quad biking
☐ Off-roading
☐ Mountain biking
☐ A bed and breakfast where no one knows your name

11. What would be your partner's reaction if you wanted to go away for the weekend with your mates?

☐ Offer to help me pack
☐ More 'Me' time
☐ Don't leave me!
☐ Change the locks

12. If a black cat crossed your partner's path while they were out, would they see this as an omen?

☐ Definitely
☐ Depends on their mood
☐ Never
☐ Wouldn't even notice the cat!

13. Does your partner ever refuse to walk under ladders?

☐ Yes
☐ No
☐ Depends where the ladder is

14. Does your partner ever avoid stepping on the cracks in the pavement when out walking?

☐ Always
☐ Occasionally
☐ Never
☐ Only if there are bears in the area

15. What would your partner do if someone lit a cigarette in a no smoking area?

☐ Ignore it
☐ Cough loudly
☐ Ask them to put it out
☐ Offer an ashtray
☐ Try and cadge one

16. How has the smoking ban in pubs affected the frequency with which your partner goes for a drink?

☐ Not affected
☐ They go more often
☐ They go less often
☐ Only a drinking ban would make a difference

17. Given a map and compass, could your partner find their way on foot across Dartmoor?

☐ Easily
☐ Quite easily
☐ With difficulty
☐ Wouldn't even get out of the car park

18. What does your partner do when a car tyre is punctured?

☐ Mends it
☐ Rings for help
☐ Abandons the car
☐ Buys a new car

19. Which of these types of holiday would your partner most enjoy?

☐ Beach
☐ City break
☐ Skiing
☐ Walking

20. If another driver cuts your partner up on the motorway, which of these are they most likely to do?

☐ Ignore it
☐ Wait until they get a chance to do the same
☐ Flash their lights
☐ Swear

21. An angry driver, who has been cut up, berates your partner; how do they react?

- ☐ Ignores them
- ☐ Shouts back
- ☐ Punches them
- ☐ Pretends you were driving

22. You are queuing in the post office and someone pushes in. How does your partner react?

- ☐ Not bothered
- ☐ Complains
- ☐ Moans to you
- ☐ Confronts the queue-jumper

23. What is your partner's idea of a perfect day out on a summer weekend?

☐ Country picnic
☐ Day trip to Paris
☐ Museum/exhibition
☐ Shopping

24. Your partner is waiting for you in a restaurant and you have to cancel. What do they do?

☐ Order alone
☐ Leave
☐ Invite a friend
☐ Eat anyway and charge the meal to your card

25. Which of these would your partner prefer from the dessert menu?

☐ Chocolate mousse
☐ Apple crumble
☐ Sorbet
☐ Fruit salad

26. Which of these would your partner prefer as a main course?

☐ Dover sole
☐ Fillet steak
☐ Duck à l'orange
☐ Lasagne

27. Who would your partner prefer to go on holiday with?

- ☐ Just you
- ☐ Another couple
- ☐ A big crowd
- ☐ The dog

28. Which band would your partner kill to see live in concert?

----

29. When shopping for clothes, which is your partner's favourite high-street store?

----

30. Which of these adventure holidays would appeal to your partner most?

☐ African safari
☐ Rock climbing
☐ Deep-sea diving
☐ Rafting

31. Browsing in a department store, in which of these sections would your partner linger longest?

☐ Beauty
☐ Fashion
☐ Furniture
☐ Mirrors
☐ Electronics

32. Would your partner give up a seat on a crowded bus to someone more in need of it?

☐ Always
☐ Depends on their mood
☐ Never
☐ Who goes on buses?

33. Which shared leisure activity does your partner enjoy the most?

----

34. What does your partner do if you are in a restaurant and the service is very slow?

☐ Doesn't notice
☐ Ignores it
☐ Gets stressed
☐ Complains
☐ Walks out loudly telling anyone who'll listen

35. Which of these would be a priority in a holiday villa?

☐ Private pool
☐ Private beach
☐ Private location
☐ Private dancer

36. How does your partner react to clutter in the workplace?

☐ Needs to tidy
☐ Not bothered
☐ Adds to it
☐ Gets someone else to sort it out

37. How does your partner feel in a huge crowd?

- ☐ Comfortable
- ☐ Terrified
- ☐ Claustrophobic
- ☐ Excited

38. What would be your partner's attitude if you suggested going to a 'swingers' party?

- ☐ Horrified
- ☐ Very interested
- ☐ Curious
- ☐ Tell you to have a good time
- ☐ Kick you out

39. What is the worst driving offence your partner has ever committed?

----

40. No matter how trivial, has your partner ever been guilty of shoplifting?

- ☐ Never M ✓
- ☐ Once when a child D ✓
- ☐ They've never paid for anything they don't have to

41. How often does your partner return the supermarket trolley to the trolley park?

- ☐ Never D ✗
- ☐ Always
- ☐ Sometimes M ✗
- ☐ Only if I won't push them round in it

42. When dining out, what is the maximum your partner would be willing to spend on a bottle of wine?

☐ £10–£20 D M ✓✓
☐ £20–£30
☐ £30–£70
☐ More than £70

43. If your partner is away from home, how often are you likely to get a phone call?

☐ Daily
☐ Every other day
☐ Once with luck D M ✓✓
☐ When they run out of cash
☐ When they dial a wrong number

44. Which of these would your partner be most likely to order in a pub?

☐ Pint of beer
☐ Gin and tonic
☐ Alcopop   D M X X
☐ Glass of wine

45. Which of these would your partner prefer to visit?

☐ Garden centre
☐ Farmer's market
☐ Art gallery
☐ The in-laws   M D X X

46. What is the biggest lie your partner has ever told in a job interview?

Qualifications / knowing

47. Which of your partner's qualities would an employer find most impressive in a job interview?

Confidenal   hardworking
Bubbly.

48. You are having a Mediterranean holiday; what sort of accommodation would your partner prefer?

☐ Hotel   D M
☐ Self-catering
☐ Tent
☐ Caravan

49. If your partner had the opportunity to live and work in a foreign city, where would they choose?

paris / paris

50. Which dance would your partner be most likely to learn at a dance class?

----

51. Which stand-up comedian would your partner pay to see?

----

52. When you arrive at a hotel bedroom, what is the first thing your partner does?

- ☐ Bounces on the bed
- ☐ Unpacks   M ✗
- ☐ Checks out the TV D ✓
- ☐ Undresses

53. How often does your partner thank another driver who lets them through?

☐ Always
☐ Never
☐ Depends on mood

54. Which of these would your partner prefer in order to take some exercise?

☐ Gym
☐ Jogging
☐ Team sport DꝺMX
☐ Sex

55. Would your partner be happy to take part in a séance?

☐ Yes, they would enjoy it
☐ Yes, but with trepidation
☐ No, it's dead scary
☐ No, it's a load of bunkum

M
S

56. How does your partner greet their female friends when you are out?

☐ Hug
☐ Three kisses
☐ Peck on the cheek
☐ Shakes hands

57. Which song would your partner be most likely to perform at a karaoke night?

☐ 'My Way'
☐ 'You Sexy Thing'
☐ 'Amazing Grace'
☐ 'How Much Is That Doggy in the Window?'

58. How many times has your partner taken a driving test?

---

59. Which was the last film you saw in the cinema that made your partner cry?

---

60. When you travel by plane, where does your partner prefer to sit?

☐ On the aisle
☐ In the middle
☐ Window seat
☐ In the departure lounge

61. If you were to travel on a double-decker bus, where would your partner prefer to sit?

☐ Top deck
☐ On the bottom
☐ Wherever there are least screaming children
☐ They would never travel on a bus

62. When in a restaurant, how tolerant is your partner when there is a screaming child at the next table?

☐ Very tolerant
☐ Grins and bears it M ✗
☐ It drives them crazy S ✗
☐ They demand to be moved

63. What does your partner do if you get lost while out driving?

☐ Find someone helpful to ask for directions S ✓
☐ Ignore everything and keep driving
☐ Rely on satnav
☐ Pull over and consult the map themselves
☐ Blame you M ✓

64. How often do you go shopping together for the weekly groceries?

☐ Never
☐ Sometimes
☐ Always
☐ We have them delivered

65. Which of these would your partner most like to feel when out?

☐ Wind in their hair
☐ Sand between their toes
☐ Sun in their eyes
☐ Lead in their pencil

66. Would your partner refuse to leave a tip in a restaurant if the service was bad?

☐ No, they are too polite
☐ Yes, and they would make a point of making
sure everyone knew why M X
☐ Yes, but they'd leave quickly before anyone
notices S X
☐ They're too mean to tip in the first place

67. Does your partner carry a photograph of you in their wallet/purse?

☐ No, I hate having my photo taken
☐ Yes, a naughty one! Yes X
☐ A very out-of-date one
☐ No, just one of themselves yes

68. If surrounded by aggressive football fans, would your partner pretend they supported the same team?

☐ Yes, they're a wimp!
☐ No, they would ignore them   S
☐ No, they hate football   M

69. Which of these is most likely to make your partner go 'Aww!'?

☐ Baby
☐ Puppy   MS
☐ Kitten
☐ Photograph of themselves

70. What was the last play your partner saw in the theatre?

----

71. Which of these would your partner prefer to ride?

- ☐ Motorcycle S X
- ☐ Surf board
- ☐ Elephant M
- ☐ Horse
- ☐ You

72. How punctual is your partner for appointments?

- ☐ Always on time
- ☐ Bit late
- ☐ Always very late S
- ☐ Everyone else can wait for them M

73. In wet weather, how does your partner usually try to keep their head dry?

☐ With a hood
☐ With a hat
☐ With an umbrella
☐ Doesn't bother

74. It is said that your choice of car reflects your sexual drive. What does your partner's choice say about them?

----

75. You have won a week's holiday for two in a nudist camp; how would your partner react?

☐ Refuse to go on principle
☐ Take the free flights and check into a hotel
☐ Pack a toothbrush and go for it
☐ Invite your sexiest neighbours to come along and join in the fun

MS
XX

Mr & Mrs Past, Present and Future

Ever wish you could turn back the clock on your relationship ... Or speed it up?! Mr & Mrs is about to go back to the future to test your knowledge on 'who was her first kiss?' or 'what did he want to be when he grew up?' Find out the answers to these questions and more in 'Mr & Mrs Past, Present and Future'.

nel 39
para 34

1. Which of these describes your partner's knowledge of your previous love life?

☐ Too precise for my own good
☐ Very vague
☐ Approximate
☐ Not interested

2. Which three people would your partner want on their life raft?

(handwritten notes)

3. If you were choosing a new home, which of these would be most important to your partner?

☐ Distance from the pub
☑ Kitchen ①
☐ Garden
☐ Décor

4. When buying a new car, which of these would be most important to your partner?

☐ Fuel consumption
☐ Colour ①
☐ Engine capacity
☐ Will they look cool in it?

5. Given the opportunity, would your partner travel to the Moon?

☐ No way! ①
☐ Only under duress
☐ Would jump at the chance

6. If your partner could have any other career, what would it be?

artist ①   animator

7. What does your partner believe happens when you die?

Soul goes on ① " " " " ①

8. What would your partner like to be reincarnated as?

— ①

☐ Man
☑ Woman ①
☐ A fluffy kitten

9. If your partner could buy any car, what would it be?

Smart car Ⓧ   Audi TT ①

10. Does your partner believe in horoscope predictions?

☐ To the letter   ✓ ①
☑ Only if they are good ①
☐ Never
☐ Refuses to read them

11. How many years together will you be celebrating on your next anniversary?

2 ①   2 ①

12. What was the name of your partner's first pet?

~~————~~   mindy

PIP.

13. What was the first single your partner ever bought?

~~Take that~~ ?

14. What was the first album your partner ever bought?

~~Take that~~ Now....
①

15. How would your partner describe their childhood?

- ☐ Idyllic
- ☑ Carefree
- ☐ Contented
- ☐ A long time ago

189

16. What is your partner's earliest memory?

chips on beach/
Christmas performance

dicht
understan
after chi
dream

(4)

17. What was your last serious argument about?

housework   S.   D

(3)

18. What was the first film you saw together?

Nicole Kidman D
and Kid in

dicht finish

(2)

19. Whose was the first party you ever went to together?

D
mels bi day.
(glasto.)

chris + kair
(Halloween)

190

Mr & Mrs Past, Present and Future

20. Which of the following best describes your partner's reaction in a domestic crisis?

☐ Calm and positive
☐ Screaming the place down
☐ Tearful
☑ Chucking the blame anywhere but at themselves

21. Given the choice, in which of these would your partner most like to live?

☐ City centre
☐ Suburb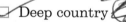
☑ Deep country
☐ Cave

22. Given the choice, which of these would your partner prefer to live in?

☐ Penthouse flat
☑ Country cottage ①
☐ Townhouse
☐ Tent

✓

23. What is the name of your partner's first school?

----

24. Who was your partner's best friend at secondary school?

Adele
----

25. What is the scariest thing that has ever happened to your partner?

bad smear cell.   motor bike accident ①
                        and in hospital after

26. If your partner could become fluent in another language, what would it be?

German   Italian
                        French

27. If your partner could do one thing to change the world for the better, what would it be?

distribute   ① "   " ①
money evenly.

28. How does your partner accept advice?

- ☐ Readily
- ☐ Reluctantly ✗ / ✓ ① ✓ ①
- ☐ Rejects it
- ☐ Won't even listen

29. How is your partner most likely to show affection?

- ☐ Words ✓ ①
- ☐ Physical touch ✓ ①
- ☐ Buy presents

30. Apart from you, who is the one person your partner can be completely natural with?

~~Danielle~~ ① ~~Giovanna~~
Donna. ① Adele ①

31. What is your partner's biggest extravagance?

~~gadgets / clothes~~

technological (gadgets ⟺ Jewlery
①   ①

32. What is your partner's blood group?

?

33. Does your partner carry a donor card?

☐ Always has done   ①
☐ Keeps meaning to get one
☐ There's nothing worth saving!

34. Are your partner's teeth their own?

☐ Yes, all of them
☐ There are a couple of false ones
☐ They are all false
☐ So I'm told!

35. Has your partner told you their email password?

yes ① *yep* ①

36. Do you know your partner's bank account PIN?

☐ Yes, we share everything ① ①
☑ No, I've never asked
☐ No, too paranoid to tell me

37. How happy would your partner be for you to scroll through the text messages on their mobile phone?

☐ Perfectly happy   ✓ ①   ✓ ①
☑ Indifferent
☐ Only after editing them

38. Would your partner be prepared to share your toothbrush?

☑ They already do!   ✓ ①   ✓ ①
☑ Yes
☐ Never
☐ I wouldn't let them

39. If your partner were to choose a new nickname for you, what would it be?

bunny ①   naughty ①

40. Which quiz show do you think your partner would fare best on?

☐ *The Weakest Link*
☐ *Mastermind*
☑ *Supermarket Sweep*

41. How would your partner prefer to pass the time on a wet afternoon?

☐ Do a jigsaw
☐ Play Monopoly
☐ Play cards
☑ In the sack

42. Which of these best describes your relationship?

☑ Love at first sight ✓

☐ Slow burn

☐ Up and down ✓ ①

☐ Amazed it has lasted so long

43. Which of your friends might your partner be happy to be in a relationship with?

Guillanna   Danni ①

44. What was your partner's very first chat-up line?

I like skiing ①   ①

- Vanya → lights
  on, no one's
  home.

- boarding
- bad back!

199

- sweat patch
- Jokes

45. Has your partner ever used an Internet dating site?

No ①   Yes ①

☐ Once and look what they got!
☐ Never
☐ They wouldn't know how to

46. Has your partner ever lied about their age?

Yes ①   Yes ①

☐ All the time
☐ Only to get a drink in the pub
☐ Never
☐ Only when pulling

47. Would your partner have a tick beside any of these 'fatal flaws'?

☐ Anger
☐ Control freak   ✓①
☐ Hasn't grown up   ✓①
☐ Emotionally remote

48. If your partner discovered you were unfaithful, what would be the reaction?

☐ Leave you   ✓①
☐ Forgive you
☐ Shred your clothes ✓①

49. If your partner could go back in time to any age at which they were happiest, what would it be?

When we met ①   childhood

50. If your partner could change their first name, what would they choose?

Princess ①   Star!! ①

51. Which item of your partner's wardrobe can they not live without?

? Joggers ①

52. Where was your partner born?

Grimsby ①   Leicester Towers.

53. Which of these is closest to your partner's first impression of you?

☐ Drop dead gorgeous
☐ Bit of a loser
☐ Cute ✓ ✓ ①
☐ I'd better take pity on them

54. What was your partner's first paid job after leaving school or college?

childminder ①   welcome break ①

55. If your partner could change one thing from their past, what would it be?

56. What was your partner's favourite subject at school?

~~Art~~   Art ①
drama

57. Which item of your wardrobe does your partner like you in least?

grey joggers ①   her stuff !!

58. What was the worst job your partner ever had?

----

59. Your partner telephones a company and is put in a holding queue: how long will they hold for?

- ☐ 1 minute
- ☐ 5 minutes
- ☐ Over 5 minutes
- ☐ Forever as they're so stubborn

60. Where were you when your partner first said 'I love you'?

----

61. Which of these does your partner regularly lose?

☐ House keys
☐ Car keys
☐ Their patience
☐ Their head

62. How did your partner behave at the beginning of your relationship?

☐ Hotly pursued me
☐ Had to be wooed
☐ Played hard to get
☐ Come and get it!

63. How many points does your partner currently have on their driving licence?

----

64. Is your partner happy when you announce that your mother is coming to stay for a few days?

☐ Yes, they are the best of friends
☐ Not bothered
☐ Breaks out the crucifixes and garlic
☐ Counters by inviting their mother too

65. What is the star sign of your partner's mother?

----

66. If your partner were to go to university as a mature student, what would they like to study?

----

67. Would your partner ever consider laser eye surgery if their sight started to fail?

☐ Definitely
☐ Depends on price
☐ No way!

68. Which of these best describes your partner?

☐ Curvy/voluptuous
☐ Athletic and toned
☐ Slim
☐ Just right

69. Does your partner believe in extra-terrestrials?

☐ Definitely
☐ Only on *Doctor Who*
☐ No way!
☐ Lives with one

70. How happy is your partner to lend money to friends?

☐ Lends readily
☐ Lends grudgingly
☐ Never lends money

71. What is your partner's biggest regret in life?

----

72. Which historical figure does your partner most admire?

----

73. Who did your partner have their first grown-up kiss with?

----

74. What is the best present your partner has ever been given?

----

75. Which public figure would your partner like to have removed from office?

How Well did you Do?

How Well do you Really Know your Mrs/Mr?

0–19   Er – you have met before you started
        answering this?
20–39   You are like ships passing in the night
40–69   A bit more homework needed!
70–89   You really take note of what your partner
        does
90+   There are really are no secrets between
        you two!

Mr & Mrs in the Kitchen

0–9   Shocking! You must now do all the washing up for a week

10–29   You are no Jamie Oliver

30–49   Maybe you should just get a takeaway?

50–69   Watch out Gordon Ramsay – you really know your way around the kitchen, well done

70+   Well done, you just earned yourself a romantic dinner cooked and prepared by your partner ... enjoy!

Mr & Mrs in the Bedroom

0–9	Maybe you should read the *Kama Sutra*?
10–29	Sorry, honey, I must have fallen asleep
30–49	Not tonight darling, I have a headache
50–69	That's the spot
70+	Ding dong!

Mr & Mrs Out and About

0–9   Poor show, you owe your partner dinner out – and you're paying!

10–29   You need to spend more alone time with your loved one

30–49   Almost good enough ... but not quite. Why not plan a weekend away?

50–69   Impressive stuff, most partners could learn a thing or two from you

70+   Gold star for you! Your partner owes you a romantic dinner for two and the bill's on them

Mr & Mrs Past, Present and Future

0–9   You've got a memory like a goldfish!!

10–29   Have you suffered a bash on the head
           recently?

30–49   Maybe you should listen to your
           partner some more if you want the top
           scores

50–69   Well done super brain, but you can still
           improve

70+   You truly know your partner inside out.
           The least they can do is surprise you with
           a gift this week